JOHN ON...

REFLECTIONS ON AN
UNUSUAL GOSPEL

STUDY GUIDE

John on...
Reflections on an Unusual Gospel

STUDY GUIDE

Terry Young

PREFACE

This study guide is intended to be used in groups and in conjunction with the main text: *John on… reflections on an unusual gospel.* The themes of these studies follow the chapters in the book and the questions here are found at the end of each chapter in the book.

John on… was written to help people engage with John's gospel for themselves and these studies bring the questions from the book together in a format for joint discovery as groups of people ask themselves the questions and collectively set about answering them.

This is not a book that takes you through John chapter by chapter: the readings provided illustrate the theme, but they will not provide all the background needed. You will need, then, to prepare ahead of time (and more of that below). However, it is not a standard topical analysis of John, either. It is an attempt to catch the things about Jesus that grabbed John's attention so completely that when he wrote it down decades later, he produced an astonishing and mysterious narrative. The themes dance in and out of one another, so you are likely to encounter some ideas several times as you make your way through the studies – catching each in a different light as you glimpse it from different perspectives.

INTRODUCTION

How to use this material

Preparation adds to any learning or group activity. If you are part of the group, why not read the passages suggested for each study and simply reflect on them? You might like to read the passages each day for a few days before the group meeting. Next take a question and think about it.

I don't know when you find it easiest to reflect – in the shower, on the bus, waiting outside the school gates, at the bank or somewhere else. Try having one or two of the questions in your head to turn to at those times and use those ideas to fuel your contribution when the group gets together.

If you have time for some more formal preparation, why not look up the passages in a commentary? If you do not have a commentary, it might be worth thinking about buying one. There is plenty of material online, too – videos, teaching notes, devotional contributions and some commentaries. I have found Bible Hub a good site to turn to, but there is no shortage of excellent resources.

Since this is not a chapter-by-chapter study, you will have to range beyond the suggested passage, which has been chosen because it illustrates the theme under consideration. There will be other examples of the same idea in John, precisely because it is a theme! The easiest way to take in the sweep is to read the whole gospel through quickly, maybe several times, or even to put on a recording of the gospel in the car: I particularly enjoy listening to David Suchet as he reads.

When you get to the group, please try to contribute and to listen to what others contribute. Groups tend to find their own dynamic: some may gravitate to robust debate around startling ideas, while others may simply enjoy sharing stories about God's goodness and seeing how those experiences illuminate the passages being studied. Most groups will have an agenda that might include other things – maybe a meal, probably time to pray together and perhaps some pastoral discussion. With good timing and leadership, these other activities can enhance and even facilitate the discussion.

Making the most of the questions

It is easy to become a slave to the questions – to feel you must address them all, or that each one has a correct answer. The truth is, you can have a wonderful time discussing just one question and still reach no firm conclusions. It's not about numbers or answers. The important thing in any Bible study on John is to leave with a deeper understanding of who Jesus is and a greater commitment to an everyday relationship with him. If the questions make that possible, it does not matter how many or how few an individual or a group tackles.

Perhaps it is worth saying that the best questions help you think: they may help you focus down to produce a concise answer or they may open up an issue in entirely unexpected ways. The questions in this study are a mix. There is also a mix of styles, in the hope that what does not work for one person may work for another: the person who likes to track words through the Bible may not enjoy something more reflective or experiential – and vice versa. Some people like theology, some like personal stories. There should be something here for everyone.

The hardest thing is to decide whether questions are too easy or too hard. There are few, if any, 'easy' questions in the traditional sense of looking up a reference and writing down a few words. On the whole, the questions here are designed to work in discussion, where lots of people have something to contribute. There is nothing quite like listening to someone who has interpreted a question in a completely different way, to open up your own understanding.

One criticism of some of these questions is that they are too hard. Some questions in these studies are certainly difficult and I don't know how I would answer all of them myself. Whether this makes them too hard, however, is tricky for me to say. Some may be too hard for me to answer to my own satisfaction or they may be too hard for you to address now. The wider the range of experience in the group, the less likely it is that any question will prove too difficult for the group.

Most questions are linked to the book, so if in doubt, try to skim the chapter concerned.

The last thing is that questions are full of surprises. I suspect that some questions will prove to have unexpected short-cuts. Those questions, for instance, that try to establish some background (such as locating episodes of glory in the Old Testament) would have been quite difficult for all but the most enthusiastic Bible scholar up until maybe 15 years ago. Now most regular smart-phone users will be able to bring the material together in a few minutes of searching.

Leading a study group

If you are leading, it might help to acquire a copy of *John on...* and read each chapter ahead of time. Leading well is difficult: you prepare and want to serve up your exquisite meal, but it is a picnic where everyone has brought something! On the other hand, if nobody seems to have anything to share, the silences can stretch and brood, and people go home hungry.

Don't be afraid of silence, especially at the start. Many groups that are slow to start can be hard to draw to a conclusion once everyone has warmed to the topic. Breaking a question down, or asking a simpler version of a question, can help to get started. If it is still hard to get going, sometimes it is helpful to pick on a person and ask what they got from the question or what it makes them think of. Usually the worst thing to do is to jump into the silence by trying to answer the question yourself. Once the discussion has started, however, you can feed your preparation in as a follow-on contribution, or to illustrate the points others have made.

Steering a group can be tricky, especially if a dominant individual looks like taking the discussion off in an undesirable direction. There is no easy answer and the nearest there is to a golden rule is that questions are usually better than statements. If you wish to counter something or to help the group find a fresh perspective, you might pitch a question. Sometimes, if the group is really struggling, you may have to steer quite carefully. Maybe you might try, "I found this other passage... and I was wondering how it relates to what we have just been saying?"

In the end, you learn to lead groups by leading groups. When it works and everyone is fizzing with ideas and pondering deep issues and sharing authentic experiences, there is nothing to touch it. When it fails to light up, it may be memorable in the wrong way, and you will sense that everyone remembers you were in charge. Just don't lose faith in the questions. Questions asked in well-prepared groups really are the blue touch-paper. The firework will go off!

Pray, prepare, ask questions, and expect God to speak. Oh, and make sure to have fun – John is a wonderful gospel.

Study 1 | John on... The Word

Read: John 1:1-14

Setting the scene:

The Word is one of the most familiar themes in John: but what is he trying to convey?

In this study, we consider four ways in which John presents Jesus as The Word:

- The communicating Word, sent from the Father.

- The Word and the writings: what is the relationship between this Word and words that have been written down by prophets over the years?

- The Word that argues back: Jesus does not simply accept the doctrines of the legal and religious experts but argues forcibly that they have it wrong in critical areas.

- The last Word, that will judge and can call the dead to life again.

Spend some time talking through what each of these themes might mean and try to find passages in John that illuminate them for you.

Excerpt:

One of John's big ideas is about sending and being sent. There is lots of sending in John's gospel: priests and Levites are sent to John the Baptist (John 1:19), John the Baptist himself declares that he has been sent ahead of the Christ (John 3:28); the authorities send officers to arrest Jesus (John 7:32), while Mary and Martha send Jesus an SOS when their brother Lazarus is dying (John 11:3). There is even a pun about sending in the story of the blind man (John 9:7). But the biggest idea is that God sent Jesus, not only as a messenger, but as the message.

QUESTIONS

1   How might you prepare a short talk based on John's prologue, appealing to the theme of the Communicating Word, to introduce Jesus to a group of people who know very little about Christianity?

2   We think of communication in many contexts: through social sciences that we use to explore family relationships or organisations; in business, marketing, and advertising; as network technology and infrastructure that drives most modern life; as information theory, theories of knowledge and words; and in many other ways. Pick some aspect of communication that appeals to you and see how many modern ideas and metaphors fit with John's concept of the Word. What elements of our modern thinking do not really align? Why might that be?

3   Jesus tells his disciples that, just as he has been sent, he is sending them (John 20:21). As a follower or Jesus, think of three things you could do in the coming week to strengthen that reality in your own experience.

4 Your Muslim friends will see the succession of messengers, each delivering a divine revelation, in a different way to you because they see another prophet after Jesus. How does John's concept of the writings and the Word, of messengers and the message, address this issue? What kind of discussion might this help you to have?

5 Read 2 Corinthians 3:6. How does the contrast Paul draws between the dead letter and the life-giving Spirit influence your understanding of John's gospel? How does Paul's approach align well with the ideas we have explored about the writings and the Word?

6 Matthew, Mark and Luke, the writers of the so-called 'synoptic' gospels, arrange their material quite differently to John. Give an example from each (preferably not an example that they all quote) that reports Jesus speaking with power? How does this influence your understanding of the Word in John?

7 Have you ever felt you were arguing with God? What happened at the time? What did you learn from it?

STUDY 2 | JOHN ON... THE FATHER

Read: John 14:1-31;

Setting the scene:

John writes about the Father more than any other gospel writer and he writes differently. If the Word has been sent from the Father, then what is the Father like? John's big idea is that nobody can know God except through Jesus, and that to know Jesus is to know the Father.

John does not simply write down all he wants us to understand and, indeed, Jesus does not sit down and tell the disciples what his Father is like until near the very end of his life. But in his narrative, John shows how much Jesus cares about the way his Father's house is treated, how much Jesus cares about the revelation that the Father has committed to prophetic writing, and he explains how Jesus is busy doing good things because the Father, too, is busy.

Excerpt:

The story of the man born blind begins as the disciples try to work out who is to blame and as Jesus explains that the man is in this predicament as a visual aid to show off the good things that God does (John 9:3). Earlier on, and following another healing miracle, Jesus explains that his Father is 'always at his work' and that he himself is, too (John 5:17).

For most of us this comes as a surprise. Our prayers exhibit very little curiosity about what the Father is up to and if you listened, you might conclude that there is not much to do, anyway, apart from rescuing people from difficulties, some of which are quite trivial and many of which are of their own making. Maybe we have a view of a God who presides quietly above the hustle and bustle of the cosmos, a view which we probably do not adopt when thinking of any other head of state. In the real world, those heads seem to stay up late, get up early, and turn grey over disconcertingly short stays in office.

QUESTIONS

1 Use an online tool to see how many ways John 1:18 has been translated. Why do you think some translators use reproductive language (e.g. 'only begotten') and others avoid it? What truth is the verse expressing?

2 What is your favourite movie that shows you something important about the Father? Did the screenwriters and directors set out to illustrate this point, are you reading the message in afterwards, or is it simply in there because it is true and, as Francis Schaeffer used to say, all truth is God's truth?

3 What is the most cosmic aspect of your faith? How would anyone ever find out?

4 A friend of yours says that every faith is trying, one way or another, to reach the same God. Using John's arguments about lying and murder, how would you approach a discussion with that person?

5 How busy is the Father you worship and how is that reflected in your prayers? Try to remember things you have prayed about in the past week that recognise how busy the Father is and that respond with actions of your own.

6 Why was Jesus so upset about the trade taking place in his Father's house (John 2:12-17)? What would have to happen at your church for you to get as upset?

7 What sort of passion does John stir up in you about the Father? What are you going to do about it?

Study 3 | John on... The Spirit

Read: John 16:5-33

Setting the scene:

In John, The Word takes us back beyond the first creative command and forward past the last word of judgement, while the Spirit takes us to somewhere completely new, a world we cannot imagine, where people can be born all over again and where mountains and temples are not places to worship, but where we will worship in truth.

John hints at the difference the Spirit will make to the disciples, but it is not until that last meeting in the upper room that the disciples realise that they will never be alone again. They have an advocate, a special agent at work in the world around them, a teacher who never tires and is never stumped. Why? Because the Father loves them and wants them to follow Jesus and his ministry with 'greater things'.

How, then, will the disciples encounter the Holy Spirit? This is one of John's surprises, since he anticipates the moment, but when it comes, towards the end of the gospel, it is not at all what we were expecting.

Excerpt:

Jesus wants the disciples to know that they are not being left alone: they are being left in safe hands. Just as Jesus is not alone (John 8:16, 29; 16:32), they, too, will have company and support. I don't know how you read John 14:14-21, but clearly Jesus is addressing the sense of loss hanging over the disciples. They seem to know something is up even if they are only sensing Jesus' own heaviness of soul and are responding with a sadness of their own. Whatever it is, Jesus promises that they will not be left as 'orphans.' Jesus says he will come to them and yet he is leaving them! How can both be true? And the answer is that the Spirit is coming. So what is the minimum they need to know about the Spirit to survive when Jesus is gone?

1 How do you understand the relationship between the Father, the Spirit and the Word?

2 How do we see the Spirit in our world and what do we not see at all?

3 How does John explain what the Spirit does in the lives of people who are not yet disciples? How much of that can we see and how much can we not see?

4 Follow through the references connecting the Spirit with Truth – what is Jesus saying to the disciples there?

5 Use an online source or concordance to find the passages on the Spirit as advocate. Are there passages (perhaps beyond John's gospel) that identify Jesus as our advocate? What does this tell us?

6 Give three to four examples of how you have experienced the Spirit as your teacher? Have you any other aspects of care that you have experienced from the Spirit? Tell the story.

7 What are the 'greater things' (John 14:12) that Jesus had in mind? What has your experience of those been?

STUDY 4 | JOHN ON… BELIEF

Read: John 5:1-47

Setting the scene:

Although John has written his gospel to help people to believe in Jesus, he does not have a straightforward view of belief. The disciples come to believe and then in other circumstances, we discover again that they come to believe. What has happened to the business of hearing, responding, praying the sinner's prayer and getting on with your Christian life?

Against the modern, well-packaged, conversion experience, John tells us stories of people who discover something and then discover more – layer after layer of revelation. This raises the question as to whether we can ever reach a real faith. Is belief like the end of the rainbow that we can trek towards but never reach?

Again, although John peels away layer after layer, he knows that people really do reach a satisfying conclusion. They come to believe and their lives are never the same.

This study explores ways to understand faith and asks what it was that developed in the faith of the disciples each time that John records that they came to believe.

Excerpt:

So what did these disciples believe? Three have committed themselves to following Jesus and one has made an amazing declaration of faith. It is a bit of a surprise then, to discover that Jesus' disciples came to believe in him after seeing the miracle at the family wedding (John 2:11) and perhaps a bit more disturbing to discover later in the same chapter that it was after he rose from the dead that they believed the writings and Jesus' words (John 2:22). Nor does the pattern end there. On the first Easter, a disciple, presumably John, enters the tomb, sees and believes (John 20:8). A week or so later, Thomas reaches what sounds like a conclusive position of faith (John 20:28).

QUESTIONS

1 Use the string (sequence of lettets), 'belie' to search through the English text of John. This will take you to all of the following words in John: 'belief', 'believe', 'believed', 'believes' and 'believers'. What does this tell us about John's interest in believing? What do you make of the fact that there are no hits for 'belief' in John? What online sources can you find to help understand the words John uses (e.g. http://catholic-resources.org/John/Themes-Believe.htm [date accessed 17.4.17])? How can you use such resources to enrich your Bible study and ministry?

2 What was the royal official (John 4:43-54) looking for? How about the man by the pool (John 5:1-15)? How would you describe their journeys to faith (or not)?

3 How does John narrate the developing story of Mary's faith and that of Martha? What did they believe at the start of John 11? How about when Jesus first arrives? And by the end of the chapter? To what extent does this mirror your own experience of faith?

4 'Do you now believe?' By John 16:31, what have the disciples grasped and how is their faith about to be challenged?

5 What have you learned about baptism from considering John's take on belief? Do you baptise people in good time, too early or too late in your church? What is your reasoning?

6 Do you think John would seek to classify the person who believes in the proposition that Jesus was sent to save us, but does not follow Jesus in any observable way? If so, how?

7 To what extent are we tempted to record what we can observe, rather than to wait for the fruit of faith to become unmissable?

STUDY 5 | JOHN ON... SIGNS

Read: John 6:1-60

Setting the scene:

As your commentary, or a quick search online will tell you, many scholars find it helpful to divide the main body of John's Gospel – after his introduction (John 1:1-18) and before his summing-up stories (John 21) – into two, roughly equal, sections: a 'book for signs' and a 'book of glory,' or 'passion,' with the split at the end of chapter 12. As we have come to expect with John, the divide is not complete (since there is glory before it and there are signs that follow), but it shows how important this sequence is to John's story and to his revelation of Jesus, so much so that he begins by counting the signs off (John 2:11; 4:54). So why do they matter?

We must look in two directions to get the most from these narratives: back to Moses and around at the players in each drama: the healed, their relatives, and the crowd. Each time, who experiences what, and what impact does it make? Another way to get more from the stories is to ask why John chose these stories, since many of them are fairly mundane as miracles. When he tells us a story we knew anyway, what does he have in mind? When he tells us something new, why with that story?

Excerpt:

John is interested not just in our being convinced, but
also in our being committed to follow. The signs in John
have this same dual sense of purpose. Had they been
solely about evidence, half of them would not have been
reported, since they were not observed by the masses –
indeed, one of them could not have been observed at all,
since it occurred in two separate places. But if we think
about them in terms of who Jesus is as well as what he
can do, we may be more satisfied in our reading.

QUESTIONS

1 Following a television documentary on Jesus, one of your neighbours wants to know more and has invited you around tomorrow afternoon. He tells you that his grandson has been studying the miracles of Jesus at school and you decide to prepare by looking at the signs in John. Which one would you choose and how would you structure two or three themes to pass on to your neighbour?

2 Which of John's signs do you find the easiest and which the most difficult to believe? Why? Which is your favourite and why?

3 Take your favourite miracle from John and list all the things you learn about Jesus from it – don't be afraid to spend a few days mulling it over. What have you discovered as a result?

4 How many of John's signs would have reminded the people who first saw them of something that Moses did?

5 List the people who did not immediately recognise Jesus after his resurrection? Why do you think this was? Is this evidence in favour, or against John's assertions?

6 Why is there often a discussion associated with each of the signs? If John is out to do more than establish facts, how could you focus on one of his signs in order to develop a deeper sense of worship?

7 Do any of the signs help you to think about more effective ways to witness?

Study 6 | John on… I Am

Read: John 8:12-59

Setting the scene:

When, in our passage (John 8:12), Jesus says, "I am the light of the world," we can easily grasp something of what Jesus is claiming to be, although we might need a bit of help to work out how it fits with the passages that precede and follow the claim. There is a collection of similar statements, associated with bread, the gate, the good shepherd, and the vine, for you to track down. There are abstract formulations, too (linked to truth or resurrection), that make simple sense to use – and, indeed, we are quite happy to put these sayings into our Sunday School syllabuses.

These sayings, however, are not just child's play, and again, it pays to look back to Moses and to listen around the crowd to work out all that is going on. You may need help from a commentary or online to grasp the grammar that drives the explosion in the last two verses of our reading. This construction is used by John in a variety of ways to bring us face to face with the Jesus would sometimes rather forget – powerful and uncompromising – and to bring us closer to the Jesus we need, who is with us wherever we are and however we got there.

Excerpt:

As Moses receives his mission and instructions in front of the flaming bush, the first of many concerns that are racing around his head emerges as a question. How is God to be known – what is his name (Exodus 3:13)? Again, there are all kinds of meaning wrapped up in the word, 'name', and later in the same passage, Moses is given a different formula that is more familiar to us – the God of Abraham, Isaac and Jacob (Exodus 3:16). But the exceptional revelation that Moses receives here is to refer to God as 'I am' (Exodus 3:14). Even with this level of explanation, we have dodged around some really interesting teaching and truth, so there is plenty to go looking for.

1 The name we have as *Jehovah* or in more modern settings, *Yahweh,* uses four Hebrew letters, the nearest of which for us are YHWH. Apparently, this is closely related to the 'I am' clause. What do Exodus 3:14, Deuteronomy 32:39, and Isaiah 48:12; 51:12 tell us about God's self-disclosure to people? In what ways have you sensed the mystery or power of Jesus as 'I am' this week?

21 Why do you think the soldiers and officials fell back when Jesus says, 'I am' at his arrest (John 18:2-11)? What was Moses' reaction to the burning bush (Exodus 3:1-4:17) and are there any links between the soldiers and Moses in their reactions?

3 Look at stories in which Jesus and Moses are discussed together. How do the other gospel-writers present Jesus as being fundamentally different? How does John take a fresh approach.

4 Spend a little time looking at the 'I am' statements that are followed by 'the...' and see how many ways there are to group them. What do the different ways of grouping them teach you about Jesus? What is the most helpful part of the exercise?

5 Why do you think there is no 'I am' statement that relates to the water of life? Using passages from John 4 and 7, explain the links that John wishes to make about water, life and the Spirit.

6 What is the context in which to understand Jesus' saying, 'I am the light of the world' (John 8:12)? Use a commentary or go online to work out whether it is the festival reported in John 7, the incident with the woman caught in adultery (John 8:1-11), or the argument that develops into John 8. It may take a little research, but what do you come up with? What has drawn you to that conclusion? How do you now understand the saying?

7 CS Lewis (search online and read some of his books, if you haven't done so already) developed an argument in which he said we were forced to one of three conclusions about Jesus – either he was mad, bad, or God. What does John's sequence of 'I am' statements contribute to this analysis? How helpful do you find this?

Study 7 | John on… Glory

Read: John 17:1-26

Setting the scene:

John relates some surprising stories about glory. He tells us, for instance, about a wedding feast that was about to go horribly wrong and then, when almost nobody was watching, Jesus did something remarkable (John 2:11). John understands this to be a revelation of glory. Another time, he is relating an argument between Jesus and members of the crowd, where Jesus links glory to death by crucifixion (John 12:23-33). Still other examples come from a prayer Jesus makes (e.g. John 17:1-5). We struggle with some of John's ideas of glory and want to pull back from others, so this study aims to help with this.

John is at his mysterious best when he talks about glory, and so our challenge is to make sense of his take on glory. Fortunately, he has left us a lot of material to help us see what he saw.

Excerpt:

GK Chesterton said that if a thing was worth doing, it was worth doing badly, and church banners may bear him out. While some are creatively designed and skilfully produced, many bear a different hallmark. However, even a basic construction can deliver something profound and memorable. I recall a simple banner which said, 'GLORY to GOD.' The word 'GOD' appeared in a bright circle, with the word 'to' above the circle, and above that, like the roof on a house, the letters of the word, 'GLORY,' with the 'O' at the apex. As I looked at it, I noticed that this arrangement placed the letters 'L' and 'R' from 'GLORY' at the same level, the 'L' on the left and the 'R' on the right. This banner rescued me on more than one occasion from whatever was supposed to be going on, as soon as it occurred to me that there is a left-handed and a right-handed side to glory, with John. In fact, I think this two-sided idea about glory is very helpful in unlocking his views on the subject.

QUESTIONS

1 What glory stories in Exodus, Leviticus, Numbers and Deuteronomy may have influenced John's writing on glory? What allusions does he make directly or indirectly? You may have to use some online sources to find these connections and to think them through.

2 Read Isaiah chapters 6 and 53. In what ways do you think Isaiah's writing has influenced John?

3 For those who have studied the War Poets (and there is plenty online for those who have not) what connection do they make between death and glory? What other war poetry can you think of that contrasts with their views? Is any of this relevant to John's take on glory?

4 What connections do films about war make between death and glory. What films have something to say that might chime with John's approach?

5 To what extent have the two sides to glory been linked in your life and experience? What elements of John's glory do you feel you have already experienced or seen at first hand? What choices might we make with our time and money that would draw us into a deeper experience of glory?

6 John's view of glory delivers us from the question, 'Why me?' when we encounter bad times. How can a godly understanding of suffering help us to make the most of difficult times?

7 From John's other writings – especially in Revelation – how has Jesus prayer in John 17 been fulfilled. What is Jesus doing in glory now?

Study 8 | John on... Light and Darkness

Read: John 3:1-21

Setting the scene:

The theme of light and darkness is one of the most accessible in John's gospel. His introduction (John 1:1-18) sets the agenda with illumination that darkness cannot quench, while the last narrative he records starts early in the morning after a failed night of fishing (John 21). In between are people who come to visit under cover of darkness, or for whom daylight finally breaks when they can see for the first time. In the end, Judas slips into the night, while Jesus' arrest is lit with torches.

Beyond the brilliance of such narrative, however, what is John trying to tell us? Certainly, the motif is a metaphor, or rather it breaks into a set of diverse metaphors, moving apart every time we think we are on top of what he is saying. It is hardly surprising, then, that these metaphors do not always stack up as we might expect: belief against condemnation; living in truth against doing evil; knowing against thinking you know; new birth against death. Paradoxically, there is danger for some in revealing the light and comfort for others in shrinking back into darkness.

The idea of a witness is surprisingly central to John's whole gospel. It is important here, from John the Baptist, in telling the tale of the blind man (John 9) and relating the evidence of the anonymous, probably eponymous, bystander at the cross (John 19:35). In later studies, we will encounter many people whose stories and conversations John passes on to us, but the point here is that they have each seen something and for most of them, it has broken their darkness forever.

Excerpt:

From the start, John is making connections – the light and the witness, for instance. I had always assumed that Mark starts with John the Baptist because he is so keen to get on with the story, but John is not under the same pressure and yet he does the same thing – he cannot allude to the darkness or describe the light without a witness. Clearly John the Baptist is a much more important character than many of us allow. However, John is also emphasising the visibility of the light – you cannot have a witness if there is nothing to see.

QUESTIONS

1 When the Pharisees argue with the man who was blind in John 9, how much of what they know is not true? How does the man who was blind find ways to refute their so-called knowledge?

2 George Berkeley in the eighteenth century asked whether if a tree fell but there was nobody around to hear it, would it make a sound (read up or go online)? How does John's idea of a witness align with this philosophical question?

3 How has your experience of the light been reflected in the evidence of your witness in the past year?

4 As a disciple, how can you be light and truth in your environment? Looking back over the past week, to what extent have you been successful? What might you try next week?

5 What topics are dangerous to discuss in your circle of friends or colleagues? How does John's gospel give you courage to raise them? What will you do next time the topic comes up – even if it is only being trashed or dismissed by a colleague?

6 Are you enjoying life to the full (John 10:10)? If so, how have you gone about it? If not, what might you do to get closer to it?

7 When was the last time a friend, neighbour or colleague approached you cautiously to ask about something sensitive? How did you handle the discussion? In the light of John's narrative, what might you try next time?

STUDY 9 | JOHN ON... THE HOUR

Read: John 12:20-36

Setting the scene:

John has many ways to draw the reader in: the texture of the light, the sequence of signs, the 'I am' statements, the interviews, and the dramatic scenes, none more so than the sad story that reaches a head as Jesus weeps and then calls Lazarus to live again (John 11:1-44). Behind all this is another device which builds tension, and it is the quiet ticking of a clock: a steady stream of references to 'the hour.'

Jesus brings it up unexpectedly with his mother at a wedding and announces it at the top of his voice to a crowd reeling from the thunder. In the upper room with his disciples in his last few hours, Jesus is still talking about the mixed feeling a mother faces in anticipating childbirth and the unmitigated joy that follows once her baby has been safely delivered. Clearly John is pointing us towards Jesus' death and resurrection, but is that all?

The curious early reference at Cana (John 2:4) rather blurs the clean lines of any analysis, and, the way the ticking links to glory, forces us to ponder more deeply. Does the hour come more than once? If so, the connection to crisis may help us to think through the role the hour might play for each of us in life, and even in death.

Excerpt:

Perhaps 'the hour' is when glory is revealed – primarily in Jesus' death and resurrection and in creating a path for salvation, put potentially on other occasions, too. That way, the first reference at Cana would be a sort of preview or a foretaste of what 'the hour' would bring when it finally came. This approach to understanding 'the hour', vague as it is, has the benefit of providing a common focus without forcing us to think of one single event in Jesus' entire life, even though there is clearly a general pattern of anticipation and then acceptance and even embrace, leading up to Jesus' death and resurrection.

1 How much of the idea of the hour do other gospel writers reveal? Where do their narratives align with John's and where does John add something different?

2 How many ways does John refer to the passage of time in his gospel? How does his approach free us from wasting time on the one hand, or wasting our lives on the other hand by being so preoccupied with saving time and being busy?

3 What does the hour teach us about Jesus' sense of purpose in life? Did he have a single aim or many aims and what was it, or what were they?

4 Is it possible for a Christian to step out and do something dangerous with a complete sense of invincibility? If so, when? If not, why not?

5 What does Jesus mean when he tells his family that, for them, any time will do (John 7:6)?

6 When was the last time the hour caught you unawares? Describe how you felt and reacted.

7 How would you like to die? How are you living to make sure that happens?

Study 10 | John on... One to One

Read: John 4:1-42

Setting the scene:

John's crowds are sketched in quickly, although John is alert to the comments that swirl, hiss and murmur through and along the edges of every crowd. By contrast, his individuals are highly articulate and drawn with care. One-to-one in conversation, John reveals a Jesus that no-one else describes, and we listen in on extended interviews, snatched conversations, and interactions with people in poverty and in power.

These encounters open two interesting lines of study with practical consequences. First, what is Jesus trying to achieve in conversation? Whether he is turning around a flippant remark by an early disciple or defending himself before the most powerful politician in the land (while again, the crowd waits in silence outside the palace), Jesus is working people away from the preconceptions and towards personal belief. Second, by sharing these exchanges with us, John shows us how committed he is to the idea that he has a rational story to tell, if only it can be told to the right person in the right way.

The big challenges for us, then, are to work out whether, like Jesus, we will put in the effort to develop a plan for presenting the wonderful news, and whether we really have sufficient confidence in the message to share it with whoever will listen.

Excerpt:

For me, the most electric encounter is near the end of John (20:11-18) and the conversation flips in just two foreign words – one a name and one a term that John transliterates. They are not our words but they send a tingle down our spine: Mary, Rabboni! Up to that point it has been a conversation that was going nowhere – Mary thinks she is speaking to the gardener but this is not her only misapprehension. In the early light of a new day, she does not yet know that a very different day has dawned and that death itself is being rolled back.

1 Give an example of hearing a voice you knew, but at a time that you were not expecting it at all. What was your emotional response? How did the encounter continue? How does that help you to understand John's narrative of the resurrection on that first Easter?

2 When Jesus first meets Martha after her brother has died, why does he focus on the theology of resurrection with her? Why does he not just tell her that it will be OK?

3 Can you give an example of a conversation you have had that followed John's pattern in which uncertainty turns into a clearer understanding and even trust? You might like to think of medical encounters, legal encounters, trips to school, and especially conversations within the family. How did the conversation go and how do conversations such as that help us to understand John's gospel?

4 The oddest, and most contested, one-to-one encounter in John starts in a crowd and ends with just two people (John 7:53-8:11). Read the story and then identify themes that you have encountered in John that are present in this story? What is different about it?

5 Where do you think Western Christians have most lost confidence in the gospel? How would John want us to turn the volume up a little?

6 Jesus' early aim seems to be to encourage questions from the other party. Why does Pilate's question (John 18:38) not work?

7 What is your game plan for sharing your faith? Is it based around you own conversion experience, the conversion of a friend or relative, or do you go back to a psalm or passage of scripture? If you do not have one, how could you develop one and how might you use it?

STUDY 11 | JOHN ON... THE DISCIPLES

Read: John 20:1-31

Setting the scene:

While John talks about the twelve, he does not even name all the disciples, yet we hear more of the discussions that Jesus had with this group from John that from any other writer. Followers are not limited to the twelve, however, and John's camera catches several women, too.

Even when describing the membership of the twelve, however, John has airbrushed his own name and that of his brother, James, from the record, while providing details about several other disciples that we do not find elsewhere. However, you will have to look elsewhere to find out more about James and John themselves. As far as this group is concerned, John is the ultimate insider: informed, anonymous, intrigued by all that is happening.

In his gospel, John paints an interplay of roles and interests among the disciples: the shirtsleeve philosopher, the networker, the loyal sceptic, those prepared to ask obvious but tricky questions. As well as helping us to make sense of the way in which their collective understanding and belief was developing, John shines a light on the dynamics of our own teams and in passing begs the question of whether we have enough networkers, or visionaries or people who will put the awkward question to the room.

Excerpt:

I don't know what preconceptions we have of the people Jesus chose to follow him, but we may be in danger of assuming that Jesus chose blank slates on which to chalk up the message that they were to take to the world. This is not really the picture John presents. Andrew was searching and got as far as John the Baptist before he was pointed to Jesus. Nathaniel was meditating – presumably about Jacob and the ladder that went into heaven, from his first conversation with Jesus – and is commended by Jesus for his high moral character. Someone else was with Andrew the day that John the Baptist pointed people out.... Whoever the person was, it sounds like there was a group of friends at the heart of the team of disciples, each of whom was searching for something more in life, a group of seekers who had developed sound spiritual habits.

QUESTIONS

1 Given the reports that the other writers provide about John as a disciple, what evidence is there that he has changed since he was a disciple with the group following Jesus? Is there evidence that some of his key characteristics may have been enhanced over the years?

2 By comparing three lists of disciples (Matthew 10:2-4, Mark 3:16-19, Luke 6:12-16) with the disciples that John names, produce your own list of the Twelve. How much can you learn from each of them?

3 Of the 15 references to Philip the disciple in the gospels, 12 are in John – the synoptics mention him just once each in their lists of disciples. Why does John focus so much more on Philip than do the others? As an example, how does John help us to identify people who might help us in our Christian faith today?

4 Try to think of a good networker in your church. How well does the church or home group leadership try to use this characteristic? What have the results been?

5 We tend to think of Peter as bring impetuous, outspoken and insightful. Provide a story from John in which he illustrates each of these characteristics. If you cannot find a match in any case, why might that be?

6 Why does Judas go down and out, while Peter is restored? What history and characteristics might have led to the different outcomes? Why does Jesus treat each one that way he does?

7 Why, even at the very end of the story, do the disciples both recognise and not recognise Jesus? Was this a physical phenomenon, or will it always be the case? Have you experienced this and, if so, how?

STUDY 12 | JOHN ON... THE RULERS

Read: John 1:19-28

Setting the scene:

The political landscape was complicated at the time of Jesus, with religious fervour that peaked at festivals and threatened to boil over in violence against the Romans, who appointed the local rulers. Interestingly, John does not mention any Herod, but he presents the Jewish establishment as the meat in the sandwich between the mob and the Romans. We sense this acutely, as John describes the trial of Jesus, in the tetchy relationship between the Jewish establishment and Pilate, who has been hauled out of bed to sentence someone for alleged mortal infractions of the law of Moses. Ironically in John, both Pilate and the High Priest get it right even when they are getting it wrong.

This difficult dynamic was bound to make the establishment suspicious of initiatives that might lead either to revolt or to further oppression and so they are quickly on the scene to interrogate John and move swiftly to assess who Jesus is and where he stands on matters related to the Law. However, Jesus does not argue in the way they expect and, far from working around their framework of knowing what God expects by reading Moses, Jesus claims to have – indeed to be – a direct message from God. Large swathes of John focus on the rising hostility towards Jesus that resulted and culminated in that overnight trial.

Before we condemn the rulers, however, it is worth reflecting on how much of the energy of modern church leaders is focused on stopping things from going wrong, rather than listening to God's message for today.

Excerpt:

The rulers would undoubtedly have found it easier to debate propositions with Jesus – his take on Moses, the prophets, the psalms. They could have worked out whether he was 'sound' or not, and if not, they could have codified exactly what his problem was. However, Jesus does not give them that opportunity. Instead, he makes claims so wild and personal that they do not really know where to begin.

QUESTIONS

1 To what extent is the experience of the Jewish leaders in starting with excessive vigilance and backing themselves into a corner of inescapable hostility a feature of any leadership? Can you think of examples from politics and even from your own church life where the same patterns emerge?

2 How can church leaders know whether something new is from God? From your own experience of leadership, or seeing through the eyes of a friend who has been a leader, can you think of an example where a leadership got it right and one where it got it wrong? How do you know which was which and what were the key features of each decision?

3 Why do Jesus' claims about himself seem particularly hard for the establishment to argue with? Consider, for instance, his claim to be from above while they are from below, or that the Father (whom they cannot see) supports all he does (e.g. John 8:23 and following).

4 Consider the leaders who put their faith in Jesus – what do you think persuaded them?

5 When Caiaphas reasons that it is better that one man die than that the nation be destroyed (John 11:49-53), John sees this as a prophecy. What did Caiaphas mean when he made the statement and what does John take from it?

6 Why do those who approach Jesus with a sense of need tend to come away with faith more often than those who want to describe Jesus as a set of facts?

7 'What is truth?' (John 18:38). Should Christians be concerned to present truth in an objective sense? If so, what truths are important to fight for today? If not, then what?

Study 13 | John on... The Crowd

Read: John 7:1-44

Setting the scene:

Although we can infer a crowd in many of the scenes John describes, he often zooms straight to an individual or a group within it. The claustrophobic crowds of the synoptics are largely absent from John's narrative, although the constituent groups – some for, some against, Jesus – come into focus as Jesus speaks to them and they answer back, and there is a modern feel of social media as these exchanges become public property and are discussed throughout the crowd and reported in places far from it.

John's two big crowd scenes (John 6 and 7) focus on sustenance and refreshment. John's narrative of how so many were fed with a few loaves and fish differs from those of the other writers, as he reports on how the discussion ranges from Moses and the manna to whether he is able to sustain people. Some people are offended by the idea of consuming a person: they have had enough, and they give up on Jesus. The first scene is in the middle of nowhere, but the second is in the temple, where Jesus makes the offer of eternal refreshment.

The first crowd is close to crisis while the second is curious, initially about whether Jesus will show up. The interesting thing is the way Jesus responds to each mood and opens up a discussion around salvation.

Excerpt:

Further around, there was a picture that looked like it had been produced by Minecraft™ (look online yourself if your children are not building their own worlds with it already). I realised that the shifting grey silhouettes in the picture were people. In fact, it was a crowd, looking with the viewer toward a central building, and I realised that John's crowd is a bit like that – it takes you a minute or two to realise that there is a crowd at all. This is often because, as we have noted, John focuses on an individual or a group within the crowd, rather than on the crowd as a whole. In John 1:19-28, for instance, there is clearly a crowd, but the dialogue is between John and representatives of the establishment.

1 Do you like John's depiction of the crowd more or less than, say, the way in which Matthew describes the crowds? If so, why? If not, why not? How does John show himself to be a master story-teller in the way he tells us about the crowd?

2 Look up Maslow's Hierarchy of Needs, which describes a set of needs that start with the basics – food, shelter – and works up to 'self-actualisation'. How does a hierarchy of this type help to classify the needs of those John encounters in the crowd and in other groups?

3 What is the relationship between 'low level' needs (for food and water) and 'high level' needs (for spiritual fulfilment) when Jesus is at work in the crowd? How should this drive our own efforts in evangelism and supporting the needy?

4 What can we learn by the fact that most of John's crowd scenes pick out a few individuals within the crowd?

5 What crises have precipitated decisions in your life? Which decisions have worked out well and which have turned out badly? What are your conclusions about making decisions in the middle of a crisis?

6 What do you think is the role of crisis in conversion? Try to consider cases where there was an obvious crisis and cases where perhaps more subtle factors were in play.

7 When it comes to matters of faith, to what extent do you think the crowd follows its leaders? To what extent do leaders follow the crowd? How might this help us to understand the role of the church in society?

STUDY 14 | JOHN ON... THE WORLD

Read: John 18:12-40

Setting the scene:

The most famous verse in the Bible is about God loving the world, but what world was or is that? John certainly thinks of the world as a place, a location – our world – but he has more in mind than that. In many of the references, it is clear that John is thinking of a world of people: the crowds, rulers, disciples, men and women that we have been studying. It is to the constituents of this world that John makes his appeal and writes his gospel.

There is even more to his idea than this, for it is also clear that John uses the tag – the world – as a sort of shorthand for a world system. Politically, and before Pilate, Jesus makes clear that he comes from a different world and his power is not based on the sort of armies that are keeping Caesar on his imperial throne. John sees this world system as being hostile to Jesus and the disciples are warned that it will be hostile to them, too.

These ideas are developed further in the letters and other writings attributed to John, but even there the analysis is not over.

The good news is that Jesus has conquered the world and that we can, too.

Excerpt:

John is very interested in the world – his gospel uses the word, 'world' 78 times, although you will have to look at the Greek – perhaps online – to pick up all the references, because the English translators have eased out a few repetitions to smooth the narrative. His gospel uses up more than 40% of the New Testament's allocation of the word, 'world' and if you include the other writings traditionally attributed to him, it is more than 50%! Clearly, we are onto something fascinating.

1 How does the tension between the Word and the world show up in your life?

2 To what extent does John's teaching on the world make you, as a Christian, confident and optimistic or cautious and suspicious of others. Outline a balanced position and explain how it could make you act differently in future.

3 Does John believe in personal evil? How about you?

4 In what ways is John's take on the world fundamentally different from his observations about the disciples, or the rulers, or the crowd?

5 To what extent have you experienced trouble in the world and victory over it?

6 Can you think of political or other regimes that have specifically aligned themselves against the Word? What has happened?

7 Is Christianity a cosmic faith?

STUDY 15 | JOHN ON... EVIDENCE

Read: John 19:1-37

Setting the scene:

All the gospel writers set out to tell a story that will change the reader, presumably because Jesus set out to persuade everyone he met that there was a better way. Sometimes we see the way Jesus worked a crowd or an interview or a conversation to create a sense of need, or hope, but John has a style all his own. He presents evidence, not simply from what Jesus said or did, but from what others wrote beforehand or whispered at the time. John's array of witnesses is spectacular and the way he uses numbers and observations is truly amazing.

Like his Master, John knows that different things will convince different people and so part of his varied style makes sure that if one line of argument fails to move the reader, maybe another will work. John knows that not everyone will be convinced – he has watched some grow cynical by exposure to amazing scenes – but he believes that the evidence is there if you really want it.

Excerpt:

However, John is not going to be able to give us technological proof. He has no time-stamping camera, nor sensors with telemetry to provide a continuous readout on temperature or chemical composition. In fact, we often forget just how young our era of instrumentation is. In *Galileo's Daughter*, Dava Sobel describes Galileo's attempts to measure the acceleration due to gravity, for instance, and you realise how crude his instrumentation was even a few hundred years ago. Without stopwatches to time falling objects, his genius lay in developing shallow ramps to roll things down, diluting the gravitational force to a point where his basic clocks could capture what was happening.

QUESTIONS

1 How many lines of argument does Luke report Jesus as using when it came to debate about the Sabbath? Try Luke 6:1-5; 6:6-11; 13:10-17 and 14:1-6. How might we apply this in our lives?

2 Go through John and pick out the references the author makes to passages in the scriptures – most modern Bibles will have them in a column down the middle of the page or at the bottom. Now group them into themes, such as direct prophecies or explanatory references, that would have furnished evidence for the early readers. How many of those do you find convincing? Describe why you find the others less convincing?

3 Starting with Peter's sermon (Acts 2:14-41) and tracking back through the passages he refers to, describe how the early Christians connected their legacy of scripture with their experience of salvation through Jesus and new life in the Spirit.

4 Does the fact that John has counted the water jars at the wedding of Cana make his narrative more convincing or not. If so, why? If not, why not?

5 What arguments might you marshal if a friend who was well-informed in science and technology complained that he or she could not accept John's narrative because of all the miracles? Which arguments would you drop, strengthen or add, if your friend was a research scientist?

6 Why types of evidence that John furnishes most appeal to you – describe them and explain why they appeal. Do you prefer the detail – each piece of evidence and the types of evidence – or the whole picture?

7 How does John answer Pilate's question, 'What is Truth?' (John 18:38).

16 | EPILOGUE

Read: John 21:1-25

Setting the scene:

The last chapter of John's gospel is a strange piece of writing: some think of it as an appendix or an addendum – maybe something he thought of later and wrote up at the last minute. In this one study, we will depart from the flow of the book by encouraging you to use this passage and to create your own study of the story that summarises all he has written. There is a sense of meeting Jesus for the first time, of freshness and mystery. There is a familiar picture of eating by the shore and even the climactic scenes of the gospel are there because while they are not mentioned, Peter cannot escape them in his conversation with Jesus.

Most importantly, the passage makes one last appeal to us, the same call that John has embedded in every chapter: to follow Jesus. John has filled pages with encounters people had with Jesus and the way in which each, whether they realised it or not at the time, made a decision to follow or not. Maybe some thought they were delaying the decision while others clearly thought they were making a very different decision.

They had to make a decision and so do we. We cannot shrug and wander off.

Excerpt:

John makes it possible for us to meet Jesus, to listen to him and see what he did, to meet the Father and to get to know the Spirit, to sense the heartbeat that drove those encounters first time around. He wants you (and me!) to keep deciding.

We cannot walk away, either. John's first aim is that we should come to faith – he hopes the evidence persuades us – you and me. And then he hopes that each one of us will do something about it by becoming a disciple and making Jesus' habits our own. Which brings us nicely to the last thing Jesus says in John (John 21:22): 'Follow me!'

Questions

There are no more questions. From here on you, make must them up and answer them yourselves.

About the Author

Terry Young is an amateur theologian who started writing in the late '90s when he worked in a research centre outside Chelmsford and was part of the leadership team at Tile Kiln, a local, independent, evangelical church. His first three books, *Jake: Just Learn to Worship*, *After the Fishermen* and *Going Global*, were published by Partnership and Paternoster Press. More recently, he has started writing again, when Words by Faith published *Making Sense of Romans When You Read it for Yourself* in 2016

His day job as an academic involves teaching project management, and particularly in finding new ways to deliver courses and engage students using emerging technologies. However, he is on sabbatical for the academic year 2017/18. His research focuses on health services: how they are organised and, again, how new technology can make an impact in yielding better care under constrained budgets.

Terry and Dani live in Datchet and worship at a Slough Baptist Church nearby. Their home is emptying, and the family spreads as far south as Hampshire and as far north as Durham. Meanwhile, their first grandchild arrived in 2017.